IMPACT
CALIFORNIA SOCIAL STUDIES

Learning and Working
Now and Long Ago

INQUIRY JOURNAL

Mc
Graw
Hill

Program Authors

James Banks, Ph.D.
Kerry and Linda Killinger Endowed Chair
in Diversity Studies
Director, Center for Multicultural Education
University of Washington
Seattle, Washington

Kevin P. Colleary, Ed.D.
Curriculum and Teaching Department
Graduate School of Education
Fordham University
New York, New York

William Deverell, Ph.D.
Director of the Huntington-USC Institute
on California and the West
Professor of History, University
of Southern California
Los Angeles, California

Daniel Lewis, Ph.D.
Dibner Senior Curator
The Huntington Library
Los Angeles, California

Elizabeth Logan, Ph.D., J.D.
Associate Director of the Huntington-
USC Institute on California and the West
Los Angeles, California

Walter C. Parker, Ph.D.
Professor of Social Studies Education
Adjunct Professor of Political Science
University of Washington
Seattle, Washington

Emily M. Schell, Ed.D.
Professor, Teacher Education
San Diego State University
San Diego, California

mheducation.com/prek-12

Send all inquiries to:
McGraw-Hill Education
120 S. Riverside Plaza, Suite 1200
Chicago, IL 60606

ISBN: 978-0-07-899397-8
MHID: 0-07-899397-0

Printed in the United States of America.

6 7 8 9 10 LMN 22 21 20

Program Consultants

Jana Echevarria, Ph.D.
Professor Emerita
California State University
Long Beach, California

Douglas Fisher, Ph.D.
Professor, Educational Leadership
San Diego State University
San Diego, California

Carlos Ulloa, Ed.D.
Principal, Escondido Union School District
Escondido, California

Rebecca Valbuena, M.Ed.
K-5 Teacher on Special Assignment/Academic Coach
Glendora Unified School District
Glendora, California

Program Reviewers

Gary Clayton, Ph.D.
Professor of Economics
Northern Kentucky University
Highland Heights, Kentucky

Lorri Glover, Ph.D.
John Francis Bannon, S.J. Professor of History
Saint Louis University
St. Louis, Missouri

Thomas Herman, Ph.D.
Project Director, Center for Interdisciplinary
Studies of Youth and Space
Department of Geography
San Diego State University

Nafees Khan, Ph.D.
Department of Teaching and Learning
Social Studies Education
Clemson University
Clemson, South Carolina

Clifford Trafzer, Ph.D.
Distinguished Professor of History
Rupert Costo Chair in American Indian Affairs
University of California
Riverside, California

Letter from the Authors

Dear Social Studies Detective,

How can we learn and work together? We learn at school. We work with people in our neighborhoods. How did people learn and work together long ago? In this book, you will read about learning and working today and long ago. You will also learn about being a great citizen!

As you read, be a detective. What do you wonder about? Write questions. Look for the answers! What are you interested in? Take notes about it. Do a project to share what you've learned. Take a closer look at photos of real people and places. Use maps to find your way!

Have fun while you investigate social studies and learn more about working and playing and learning together!

Sincerely,

The IMPACT Social Studies Author Team

WESTMINSTER RURAL POSTAL WAGON ROUTE—DELIVERING MAIL.

In the nineteenth century, mail was delivered using a horse and wagon.

Contents

Reference Sources

Good Citizens

How Do People Learn and Work Together

Our World

 **Where Do We Live?**

Our Country

What Does It Mean to Be an American?

Life Long Ago and Today

 How Has Our World Changed?

All About Work

 Why Do People Work?

Skills and Features

Reader's Theater

My Notes

Getting Started

You have two social studies books.

The Inquiry Journal

This is your Inquiry Journal. It is where you ask questions and write answers.

The Research Companion

This is the Research Companion. It is where you look for clues and find answers.

Every Chapter

The chapter opener pages ask the **EQ**, an **essential question**. They also list the topics that you will learn about.

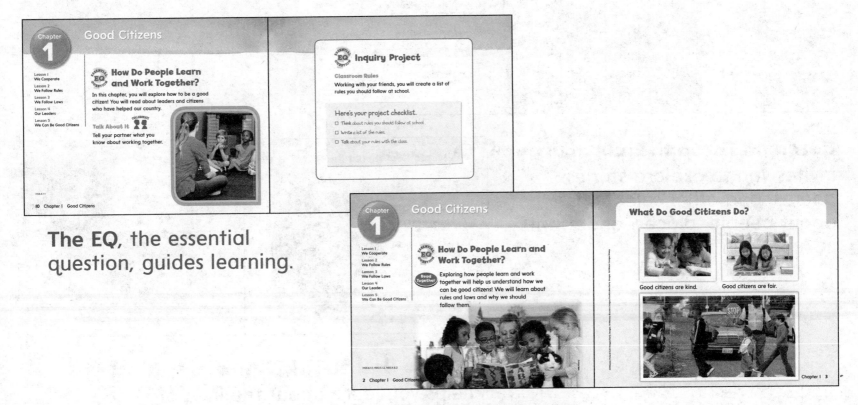

The EQ, the essential question, guides learning.

Talking about the EQ is a time to ask questions and share ideas.

Connect Through Literature

invites you to explore stories, poems, and other selections about people, places, and events in American history.

People You Should Know

helps you learn about the lives of people who have made a difference.

Every Lesson

Lessons start with a question. There is a picture for you to explore.

Learning Outcomes tell what you will learn and do in the lesson.

Lesson selections help you learn about the lesson topic and the EQ.

Analyze and Inquire

Investigate the essential question. Use your inquiry tools to look for answers.

Inquiry tools help you explore and organize new information.

Primary Sources share the words and pictures of people from the past.

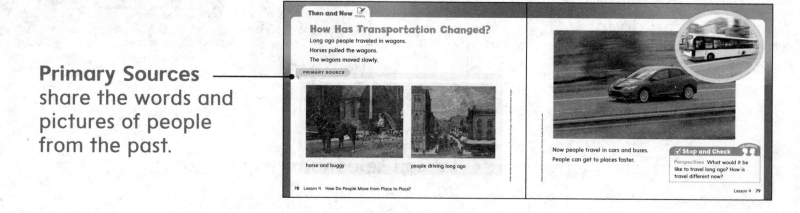

Report and Take Action

At the end of each lesson you can share your ideas about the EQ. Then you can choose an activity to show what you know.

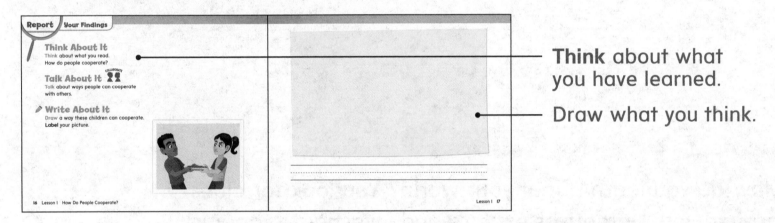

Think about what you have learned.

Draw what you think.

Think about what you read in the lesson. What did you learn about the lesson question?

Be a Social Studies Detective

How do you learn about people, places, and events? Become a Social Studies Detective!

Explore!   Investigate!   Report!

Look at Primary Sources

How do you learn about your world? You look for clues around you. Detectives explore and investigate too, just like you. One way that we can explore our world is by using primary sources.

What Is a Primary Source?

A primary source tells about or shows something that happened. It is told by someone who was there. Photographs and letters are primary sources. Diaries are primary sources too.

StasKhom/iStock/Getty Images

Look at the pictures. Ask questions.

Is it real?

Or is it make believe?

Is it a drawing?

Or is it a photo?

Talk About It
COLLABORATE

Look at the pictures. Which one is the real farmer? How do you know?

Look closely.

What do you see?

Getty Images/iStockphoto

Talk About It

COLLABORATE

Who is in the picture? What are they doing? How do you know?

Look closely at the picture.

Is it a picture from now or long ago?

Find details that help you know.

Talk About It

COLLABORATE

What are the children in the picture doing? What detail in the picture is your clue?

Explore Geography

Geographers are detectives too.

They use maps and globes to find clues.

They ask questions about the world
and where we live.

Using Maps

A map is a drawing of a place.

This is our country.

California is our state.

Talk About It   COLLABORATE

Look closely at the map.
Where is California?
What is near California?

The United States of America

13a

Using Globes

The earth is round.
A globe shows us what
the Earth looks like.

The land is green.
The water is blue.

This is a globe.

CoraMax/Shutterstock.com

COLLABORATE

Talk About It

Look closely. What are
some things you see on
maps and globes?

North America

15a

Explore Economics

People have jobs. There are many different kinds of jobs. Jobs are important for communities.

Talk About It

COLLABORATE

What kinds of jobs are these people doing? What job do you want to have when you grow up?

People long ago had jobs too. Look closely.
What job are the people in this picture doing?

Explore Citizenship

Good citizens follow rules and help others. They make our world a better place.

The words on page 19a describe what it means to be a good citizen. We can be good citizens at home, at school, in our community, and in the world.

Take Action!

Social Studies Detectives ask questions. They look for clues. Clues help us learn about our world. We can all make an impact!

This firefighter works from up in the air to put out a fire.

(l)StasKhom/iStock/Getty Images, (r)©2017 Smithsonian

Be a Good Citizen

COURAGE
Being brave

FREEDOM
Making our
own choices

HONESTY
Telling the truth

JUSTICE
Being fair
to everyone

LEADERSHIP
Showing good behavior
and being a good example

LOYALTY
Showing support for
people and one's country

RESPECT
Treating others as you
would like to be treated

RESPONSIBILITY
Being someone people can trust

How do we learn about things?

We explore.

We think.

We read.

We talk about them.

And then we find out more!

Explore Main Topic and Key Details

The **main topic** is the most important idea.
The **key details** tell us more about it.

Main Topic

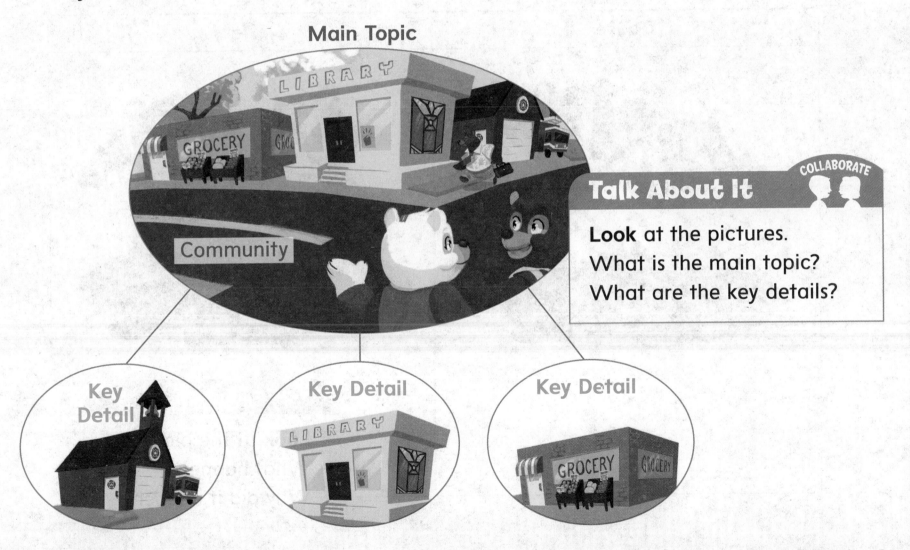

Community

Key Detail

Key Detail

Key Detail

Talk About It
COLLABORATE

Look at the pictures.
What is the main topic?
What are the key details?

Explore Cause and Effect

A **cause** is what makes something happen.
The **effect** is what happens.

Cause	Effect

Talk About It   COLLABORATE

Look at the pictures.
What happens?
Why did it happen?

Explore Chronology of Events

Chronology is the order in which events happen.
An **event** is something important that happens.
Chronology of events means the order of how things happen.
When you read, look for clues and words to help you figure out the order of events.

Talk About It
COLLABORATE

Look at the pictures.
What happens first?
What happens next?
What happens last?

Explore Compare and Contrast

We **compare** to tell how things are **alike**.
We **contrast** to tell how things are **different**.

Talk About It

COLLABORATE

Look at the pictures.

How are the car and the bus alike?

How are they different?

Explore Problem and Solution

A **problem** is something to figure out.
A **solution** is something that finds an answer to a problem.

Problem	Solution

Talk About It

COLLABORATE

Look at the pictures.
What is the problem?
What is the solution?

Explore Classify and Categorize

When you **classify and categorize**,
you look for ways that things are **alike**.

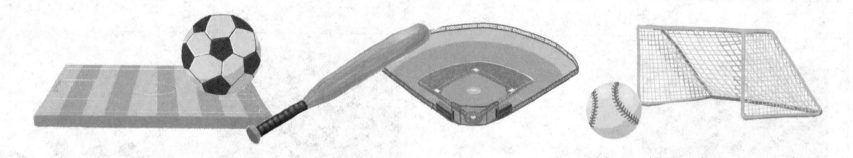

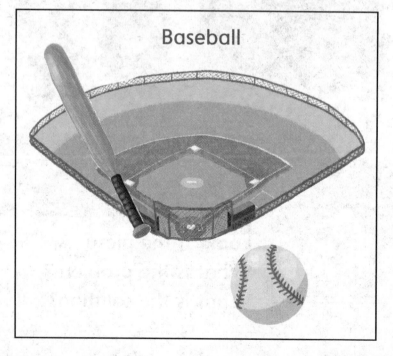

Baseball

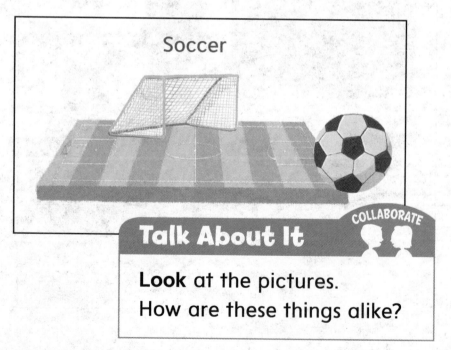

Soccer

Talk About It COLLABORATE

Look at the pictures.
How are these things alike?

ESSENTIAL EQ QUESTION

How Do People Learn and Work Together?

In this chapter, you will explore how to be a good citizen! You will read about leaders and citizens who have helped our country.

Talk About It COLLABORATE

Tell your partner what you know about working together.

Robert Kneschke/Alamy Stock Photo

HSS.K.1.1

 **Inquiry Project**

Classroom Rules

Working with your friends, you will create a list of rules you should follow at school.

Here's your project checklist.

☐ **Think** about rules you should follow at school.

☐ **Write** a list of the rules.

☐ **Talk** about your rules with the class.

How Do People Cooperate?

Lesson Outcomes

What Am I Learning?
You will explore ways people cooperate.

Why Am I Learning It?
Learning about cooperation will help you understand how to work together with others.

How Will I Know that I Learned It?
You will draw and write about a way to cooperate.

Talk About It COLLABORATE

Look closely at the picture.

What are these children doing?

HSS.K.1.1

Analyze the Source

1 Inspect

Look at the pictures.

Tell what is happening.

(Circle) what happens first.

2 Find Evidence

Look Again at the pictures.

Draw a box around what happens last.

 The Soccer Game

3 Make Connections

Talk How did the children cooperate? COLLABORATE

Why is it a good idea to cooperate with others?

4 Research Companion

Investigate Read pages 8–13 in your Research Companion.

Look for details about what happens first, next, and last.

Think About It

Think about what you read.
How do people cooperate?

Talk About It COLLABORATE

Talk about ways people can cooperate
with others.

Write About It

Draw a way these children can cooperate.
Label your picture.

What Are Rules?

Read Together

Lesson Outcomes

What Am I Learning?
You will learn what rules are.

Why Am I Learning It?
You will understand why people need to follow rules.

How Will I Know that I Learned It?
You will draw and write about a rule. You will talk about why people need the rule.

Talk About It COLLABORATE

Look closely at the picture.

What are these children doing?

What rules are they following?

HSS.K.1.1

Play with Blocks

1 Inspect

Look at the pictures.

What does the girl want to do?

Draw a box around that picture.

2 Find Evidence

Look Again at the pictures.

How do they solve the problem?

Circle the solution.

3 Make Connections

Talk What **rule** did the boy follow?

COLLABORATE

What are some other solutions? What would you do?

4 Research Companion

Investigate Read pages 14–19 in your Research Companion.

Look for problems and solutions.

Think About It

Think about what you read.
What are rules?

Talk About It COLLABORATE

Talk with a partner about what rules are and why people need rules.

Write About It

Think of a rule you use every day.
Draw a picture showing the rule.
Label your picture.

Why Do People Have Laws?

Read Together

Lesson Outcomes

What Am I Learning?
You will explore laws.

Why Am I Learning It?
Learning about laws will help you understand why people have laws.

How Will I Know that I Learned It?
You will draw about a law you followed.

Talk About It
COLLABORATE

Look closely at the pictures.

What do these signs tell people?

HSS.K.1.1, HSS.K.4.3

1 Inspect

Look at the pictures.

When is it safe to go?

(Circle) the part of each sign that tells you it is safe to go.

2 Find Evidence

Look Again at the signs.
How are they alike?
How are they different?

Read Together

How Do Laws Keep People Safe?

stop

go

Jim Barber/Shutterstock.com

walk

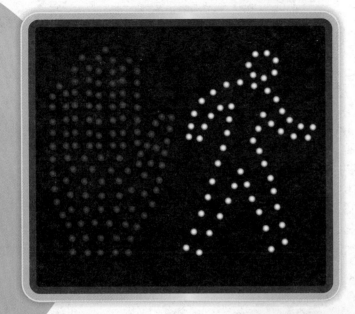

stop

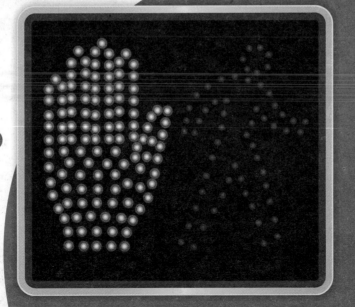

3 Make Connections

Talk How do these signs keep people safe?

COLLABORATE

What are some other signs that keep people safe?

4 Research Companion

Investigate Read pages 20-25 in your Research Companion.

Look for ways that people follow laws.

Think About It

Think about what you read.
When have you followed a **law**?

Talk About It

Talk with a partner about a law you followed.
Tell what happened.

Write About It

Draw a picture about a time when you
followed a law.
Label your picture.

Lesson 4

Who Are Our Leaders?

Read Together

Lesson Outcomes

What Am I Learning?
You will learn about different leaders.

Why Am I Learning It?
You will understand what leaders do.

How Will I Know that I Learned It?
You will draw and write about the leader you would like to be.

Talk About It
COLLABORATE

Look closely at the pictures.

Who are school leaders?

What do they do?

HSS.K.3, HSS.K.4.5, HAS.HR.2

principal

teacher

1 Inspect

Look at each picture.

Draw a box around the mayor.

2 Find Evidence

Look Again at the pictures.

What does a mayor do?

Circle details that show you what a mayor does.

Read Together

What Does a Mayor Do?

A leader is someone who helps us to make plans.

A good leader helps us do the right thing.

A mayor is the leader of a town or city.

A mayor signs important papers.

A mayor helps make the community better.

(t)©Dave and Les Jacobs/Blend Images LLC; (b)Andrey_Popov/Shutterstock.com

3 Make Connections

Talk How are a mayor and a principal alike? How are they different?

COLLABORATE

4 Research Companion

Investigate Read pages 26–31 in your Research Companion.

Think of questions about the leaders.

Look for main topics and key details.

Think About It

Think about what you read.
What do different leaders do?

Talk About It

COLLABORATE

Talk about what these leaders do.

Write About It

Which leader would you like to be?
Draw a picture of the leader.
Label your picture.

What Does It Mean to Be a Good Citizen?

Lesson Outcomes

What Am I Learning?
You will learn what a good citizen does.

Why Am I Learning It?
You will understand your role in your school, community, state, and country.

How Will I Know that I Learned It?
You will draw and write about being a good citizen.

Talk About It COLLABORATE

Look at the picture.

What do you see?

What do you think will happen next?

HSS.K.1.2, HSS.K.1.3

1 Inspect

Look at the pictures.

Circle the characters in the story.

Draw a box around the problem.

2 Find Evidence

Look Again at the pictures.

Draw a box around what the characters do.

How does the story help you know what it means to be a good citizen?

Read Together
The Lion and the Mouse

HA
HA

3 Make Connections

Talk Why does the mouse help the lion?

COLLABORATE

4 Research Companion

Investigate Read pages 32–39 in your Research Companion.

Look for ways that people are good citizens.

Think About It

Think about what you read.

What does it mean to be a good citizen?

Write About It

Draw a picture of someone being a good citizen.

Label your picture.

Talk About It COLLABORATE

Talk with a partner about your picture.

What is the citizen doing?

Inquiry Project Wrap-Up

It's time for your team to share your project! Here's what to do.

☐ Show your list.

☐ Explain your rules.

☐ Talk with your class about what would happen if you did not follow the rules.

Tips for Discussing

Remember these tips when you talk with your class.

☐ Listen when others talk.

☐ Take turns speaking.

☐ Respond to what your classmates say.

Project Rubric

Use these questions to help evaluate your project.

	Yes	No
Did we think of rules we should follow at school?		
Did we make a list of the rules?		
Did we work well as a team?		

Project Reflection

Think about your work in this chapter. Tell a partner one thing you did very well. Then tell what you learned about yourself.

The Little Red Hen

Narrator: Once there was a farm with many animals.

One day Little Red Hen found a seed.

She wanted to plant the seed.

Little Red Hen: Who will help me?

Cat: Not I!

Dog: Not I!

Pig: Not I!

Little Red Hen: I will do it myself.

Narrator: The seed grew into wheat.

Little Red Hen picked the wheat.

She made some flour.

She wanted to bake bread with the flour.

Little Red Hen: Who will help me?

Cat: Not I!

Dog: Not I!

Pig: Not I!

Little Red Hen: I will do it myself.

Narrator: The animals were hungry.

The bread smelled good.

Little Red Hen wanted to eat the bread.

Little Red Hen: Who will help me?

Cat: I will!

Dog: I will!

Pig: I will!

Little Red Hen: No, I will eat it myself.

Our World

Where Do We Live?

In this chapter, you will explore where you live! You will read about people today and in the past who made our world.

Talk About It

COLLABORATE

Tell your partner what you know about our world.

HSS.K.4.4, HAS.HI.2

FatCamera/E+/Getty Images

Inquiry Project

Our Neighborhood

Working with your friends, you will create a large map of our community.

Here's your project checklist.

☐ **Choose** important places in our community.

☐ **Make** a map of our community. Use symbols to show the important places.

☐ **Present** your map.

What Can We Find at Our School?

 **Read Together**

Lesson Outcomes

What Am I Learning?

You will explore people and things at school.

Why Am I Learning It?

You will name people, places, and things at school.

How Will I Know that I Learned It?

You will make a map of your classroom.

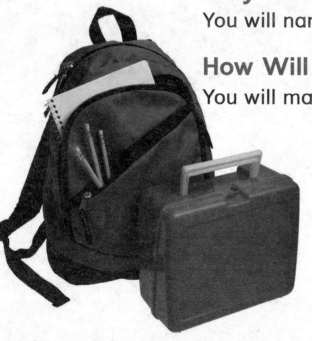

Talk About It COLLABORATE

Look at the schools.
How are they alike?
How are they different?

HSS.K.4.5, HSS.K.6.3

D. Hurst/Alamy

This is a school today.

This is a school from long ago.
This picture was taken in 1916.

1 Inspect

Read the text.

Look at the pictures.

Draw a box around things you see at school.

2 Find Evidence

Reread the text.

Circle the words that tell what to do at school.

Read Together

Welcome to Our School

Welcome to our school today!

We will learn, and we will play.

Take a look around and see,

Tell me if you will agree.

A school, a friend, a tall flag pole,

A teacher, or a swing,

A lot to see at school today.

What will tomorrow bring?

Westend6l/Getty Images

3 Make Connections

Talk What can you see at school?

COLLABORATE

How is this school like your school?

4 Research Companion

Investigate Read pages 56–63 in your Research Companion.

Look for things that are alike and different.

Think About It

Think about what you read.

What can we find at our school?

Talk About It COLLABORATE

Talk with your partner. Where are things located?

Write About It

Draw a map of your classroom.

List five things you see in your classroom.

_____

_____

_____

_____

_____

_____

Draw a **map** of your classroom. Label five things from your list.

What Is a Neighborhood?

Lesson Outcomes

What Am I Learning?
You will explore places and things in a neighborhood.

Why Am I Learning It?
Learning about neighborhoods will help you understand where you live.

How Will I Know that I Learned It?
You will draw and label a map of your neighborhood.

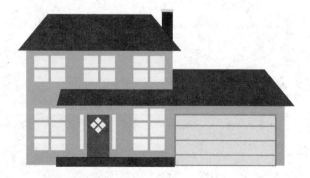

Talk About It   COLLABORATE

Look at the picture.
Where are the children?
Where is the soccer ball?

HSS.K.4.1, HSS.K.4.2, HSS.K.4.3, HSS.K.4.4, HAS.CS.4, HAS.HI.2

left

behind

right

near

in front

far

Kris Timken/Getty Images

Lesson 2   **59**

1 Inspect

Look at the **map**.

What does it show?

Draw a blue (circle) around the lake.

Draw a red (circle) around the school.

2 Find Evidence

Look Again at the map.

What places are in your **neighborhood**?

Draw a [box] around the places.

 Read Together

Neighborhood Map

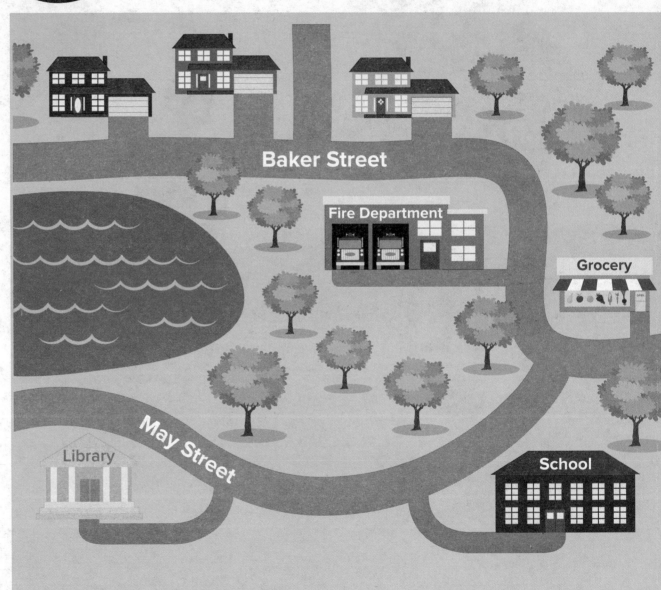

Baker Street

Fire Department

Grocery

May Street

Library

School

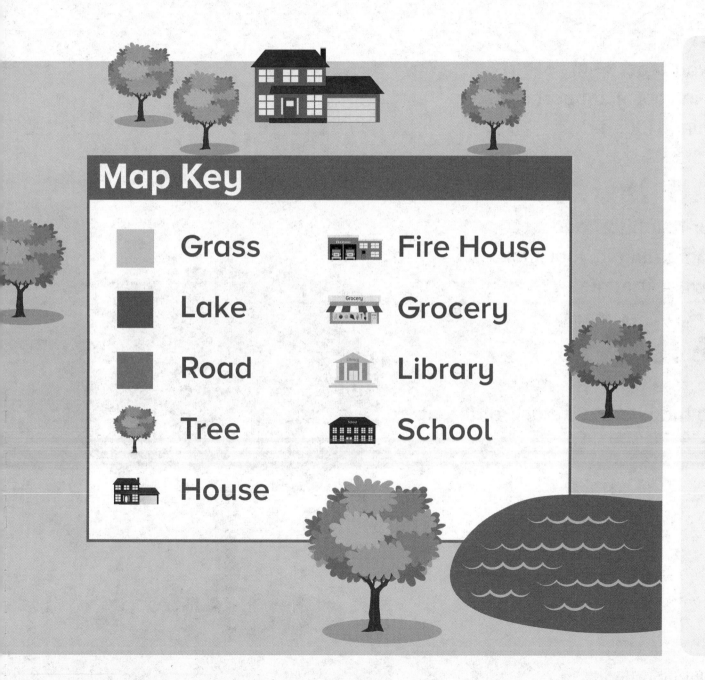

Map Key

▢	Grass	🏢	Fire House
▢	Lake	🏪	Grocery
▢	Road	🏛	Library
🌳	Tree	🏫	School
🏠	House		

3 Make Connections

Talk How is this neighborhood like your neighborhood? How is it different?

COLLABORATE

4 Research Companion

Investigate Read pages 64–71 in your Research Companion.

Look for main topics and key details.

Think About It

Think about what you read.

What can you find in your neighborhood?

Where are these things located?

Write About It

Draw a map of your neighborhood.

Write a label for something in your map.

Draw an arrow to what it names.

Talk About It COLLABORATE

Compare your map to a partner's map.

Talk about how the maps are alike and different.

Where in the World Do We Live?

Read Together

Lesson Outcomes

What Am I Learning?

You will learn about where you live in your state, country, and world.

Why Am I Learning It?

You will understand how you are part of the world.

How Will I Know that I Learned It?

You will find where you live on a map.

Talk About It   COLLABORATE

Look closely at the picture.

What do you know about Earth? What color is the land in the picture? What color is the water?

HSS.K.4.2, HAS.CS.4

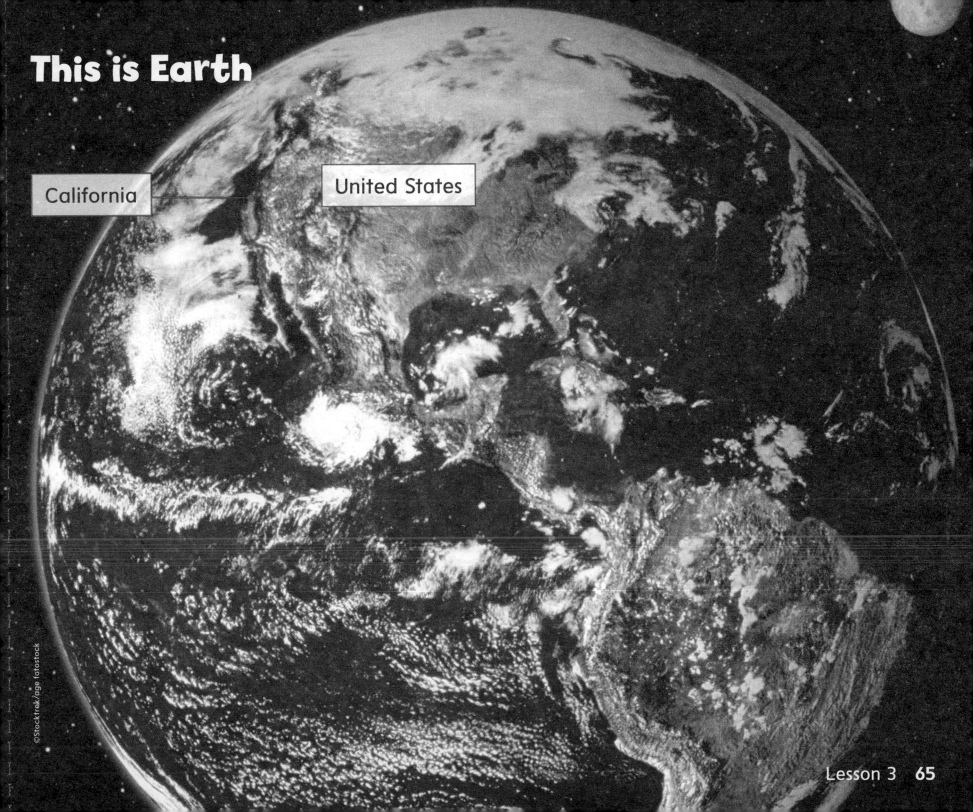

This is Earth

California

United States

1 Inspect

Read the song.

What is the song about?

How do you know?

Underline the name of the place.

2 Find Evidence

Look at the pictures.

What is America like?

(Circle) details about America in the pictures.

Read Together

"America the Beautiful"

O beautiful for spacious skies,
For amber waves of grain,
For purple mountain majesties
Above the fruited plain!
America! America!
God shed his grace on thee
And crown thy good with brotherhood
From sea to shining sea!

New York City

TEXT: Bates, Katharine Lee. "America the Beautiful." 1893. PHOTO: Image Source.

plain

sea

3 Make Connections

Talk How does the writer feel about our **country**? How do you know?

4 Research Companion

Investigate Read pages 72–79 in your Research Companion.

Look for main topics and key details.

COLLABORATE

Think About It

Think about what you read.
Where do we live?

Talk About It

Talk with a partner about how you are part
of the **world**.

Write About It

Find your **state** on the **map**. Color it.

Find your town or city.
Draw a (circle) around it.
Label the map.

How Do People Move from Place to Place?

Read Together

Lesson Outcomes

What Am I Learning?
You will learn about different kinds of transportation.

Why Am I Learning It?
You will understand how people move from place to place.

How Will I Know that I Learned It?
You will write and talk about transportation.

Talk About It

COLLABORATE

Look closely at the pictures.

What kinds of transportation do you see? How does transportation move people from place to place?

Ksenia Usata/Shutterstock.com

HSS.K.4.3, HSS.K.4.4

1 Inspect

Look at the pictures.

Which symbols can you see in your **neighborhood**?

Draw a box around those symbols.

2 Find Evidence

Look Again at the pictures.

How are the symbols alike? How are they different?

Read Together

What Do Symbols Tell Us?

A symbol is a picture that stands for something. Symbols are everywhere!

stop

school crossing

(t)Frank Lin/EyeEm/Getty Images; (b)Ken Hurst/Shutterstock.com

speed limit

railroad crossing

no
right turn

bike route

3 Make Connections

Talk What do the symbols tell us? Why is it important to obey traffic symbols?

COLLABORATE

4 Research Companion

Investigate Read pages 80–87 in your Research Companion.

Look for things that help people move from place to place.

Think About It

Think about what you read.
What signs and symbols can you see
in your neighborhood?

Write About It

Draw a **map** of your neighborhood.
Include traffic signs and important places.
Label your picture.

Talk About It

Share your map with a partner.
Talk about symbols you see in
your neighborhood.

How Can We Take Care Of Our Neighborhood?

Lesson Outcomes

What Am I Learning?

You will learn how people protect their neighborhood.

Why Am I Learning It?

You will understand why it is important to protect our neighborhoods.

How Will I Know that I Learned It?

You will draw about someone who protects his or her neighborhood.

Talk About It   COLLABORATE

Look at the picture.
What are the children doing?
Why are they doing it?

thumb/iStock/Getty Images

HSS.K.1.2

Ariel Skelley/Getty Images

1 Inspect

Look at the pictures.

What can we recycle?

Circle the pictures that show things we can recycle.

2 Find Evidence

Look Again at the pictures.

What happens when a bottle is recycled?

Draw a box around what happens first.

Read Together

Let's Recycle!

We take care of our neighborhoods when we recycle.

Recycling means to make something new from something old.

metal

plastic

paper

How a bottle gets recycled

3 Make Connections

Talk What happens when you recycle something? Why should we recycle?

COLLABORATE

4 Research Companion

Investigate Read pages 88–95 in your Research Companion.

Look for things that happen first, next, and last.

Think About It

Think about what you read.
How can we help our **neighborhood**?

Write About It

Draw a picture of someone who helps protect his
or her neighborhood.
Label your picture.

Talk About It COLLABORATE

Talk about what you drew with the class.
Tell what the person is doing and why.

fStop/Getty Images

Inquiry Project Wrap-Up

It's time for your team to share your project! Here's what to do.

☐ Show your map.

☐ Point out important places on your map.

☐ Tell about the symbols on your map.

Tips for Presenting

Remember these tips when you present to your class.

☐ Think about what you want to say.

☐ Speak loudly and clearly.

☐ Use complete sentences.

Project Rubric

Use these questions to help evaluate your project.

	Yes	No
Does our map show important places in our community?		
Did we use symbols on our map?		
Did we work well as a team?		

Project Reflection

Think about your work in this chapter. What did you do very well? What would you do next time? Tell a partner.

Chapter 3

Our Country

ESSENTIAL EQ QUESTION

What Does It Mean to Be an American?

In this chapter, you will explore special people and places in our country. You will read about ways we celebrate our state and country!

COLLABORATE

Talk About It

Tell your partner what you want to know about our country.

HSS.K.2, HSS.K.6.1

LWA/Dann Tardif/Getty Images

 **Inquiry Project**

This Is America

You will share the symbol or holiday you think best represents America.

Here's your project checklist.

☐ **Talk** with your friends about important symbols and holidays in our country.

☐ **Draw** the symbol or holiday you think best represents America.

☐ **Share** your opinion.

Why Are National Symbols Important?

Read Together

Lesson Outcomes

What Am I Learning?

You will explore symbols that represent our country.

Why Am I Learning It?

Learning about national symbols will help you understand more about our country.

How Will I Know that I Learned It?

You will draw, write, and talk about your favorite national symbol.

Talk About It

COLLABORATE

Look closely at the picture. Where have you seen this flag? What do you know about it?

HSS.K.2

Analyze the Source

1 Inspect

Look at the picture.

What colors do you see on our flag?

Circle each color you see.

2 Find Evidence

Look Again at the picture.

Draw a box around the stars.

What do the stars represent?

Read Together

The United States Flag

Our flag is a symbol for our country.

It has red and white stripes.

It has 50 white stars.

There is a star for each state in our country.

stars

stripes

3 Make Connections

Talk How does the flag represent our country?

COLLABORATE

4 Research Companion

Investigate Read pages 110–117 in your Research Companion.

Look for main topics and key details.

Think About It

Think about what you read.
What symbols represent the United States?

Write About It

Which symbol is your favorite?
Draw that symbol.
Label your picture.

Talk About It

Talk with a partner about your picture.
Why is that symbol your favorite?

Lesson 2

How Do People Celebrate America?

Read Together

Lesson Outcomes

What Am I Learning?
You will explore ways we celebrate our nation.

Why Am I Learning It?
Learning about holidays will help you understand more about what it means to be an American.

How Will I Know that I Learned It?
You will draw someone celebrating a national holiday.

Talk About It
COLLABORATE

Look closely at the picture. What are these people doing? How are they celebrating America?

HSS.K.5, HSS.K.6.1, HAS.CS.1

1 Inspect

Read the text.

Look at the picture.

What is the month?

Draw a box around the name of the month.

2 Find Evidence

Reread the text.

Look Again at the picture.

What happens on the second day of the month?

Circle the special day on the calendar.

Read Together

What Is a Calendar?

Calendars are charts that show the months of the year.
They show the weeks in a month.
They also show the days in a week.
Calendars show holidays too.

Sunday	Monday	Tuesday	Wednesday	Thursday	Friday	Saturday
	1	2	3	4	5	6
7	8	9	10	11	12	13
14	15	16	17	18	19	20
21	22	23	24	25	26	27
28	29	30				

3 Make Connections

Talk How do people use a calendar? COLLABORATE

4 Research Companion

Investigate Read pages 118–125 in your Research Companion.

Look for what happens first, next, and last.

Think About It

Think about what you read.

What are special days for our nation?

Talk About It

COLLABORATE

Talk with a small group.

How do you celebrate holidays and special days?

Write About It

Draw someone celebrating a holiday.

Label your picture to tell what happens.

Lesson 3
How Do People and Places Help Us Learn About America?

Lesson Outcomes

What Am I Learning?
You will explore special people and places in our country.

Why Am I Learning It?
You will understand more about what it means to be an American.

How Will I Know that I Learned It?
You will draw and write a story about a person or place you learned about.

Talk About It
COLLABORATE

Look closely at the picture. What do you know about this place? Why is this place important to our country?

HSS.K.2, HSS.K.6.2, HAS.HI.2, HAS.HI.3

the Statue of Liberty

GCShutter/E+/Getty Images

1 Inspect

Read the text.

What special place is this?

Circle the name of the place.

2 Find Evidence

Reread the text.

Why do people go to see Mount Rushmore?

Draw a box around the cause.

Read Together

Mount Rushmore

Mount Rushmore is a special place in our country.
It is located in South Dakota.
This is Mount Rushmore long ago.

Everett Collection Historical/Alamy

Mount Rushmore has the faces of four presidents on it.
People carved the faces into the rock.
The faces are 60 feet tall!

This is Mount Rushmore today.
Many people go to see it!

photo.ua/Shutterstock.com

3 Make Connections

Talk Why is Mount Rushmore an important place in America?

COLLABORATE

4 Research Companion

Investigate Read pages 126–133 in your Research Companion.

Look for causes and effects.

Think About It

Think about what you read.
What are special places in our country?
How have people helped our country?

Talk About It

COLLABORATE

Talk with your partner about the people
and places you learned about.
What did you learn about the people
and places?

Write About It

Choose a person or a place.
Write and draw to tell about the person
or place you chose.

How Do We Celebrate California?

Lesson 4

Read Together

Lesson Outcomes

What Am I Learning?
You will explore how we celebrate our state.

Why Am I Learning It?
Learning about ways we celebrate our state will help you understand more about it.

How Will I Know that I Learned It?
You will draw a picture of the symbol you think best represents California.

Talk About It
COLLABORATE

Look closely at the picture. What do you see?

HSS.K.2, HSS.K.6.1

Analyze the Source

1 Inspect

Look at the flag.

(Circle) the things you think are important.

2 Find Evidence

Look Again at the flag.

What parts of the flag tell us something about our state?

Draw a box around those parts.

Read Together **Our California**

We live in the state of California.

Our state is part of the United States of America.

We are proud of our state.

drmakkoy/DigitalVision Vectors/Getty Images

This is our state flag.

It celebrates California!

CALIFORNIA REPUBLIC

Viktorcvetkovic/iStock/Getty Images

1   The bear stands for strength.

2   The red stripe stands for courage.

3 Make Connections

Talk How does the flag represent our state?

COLLABORATE

4 Research Companion

Investigate Read pages 134–139 in your Research Companion.

Think About It

Think about what you read.
How do we celebrate California?

Write About It

Which holiday or symbol do you think best
represents our state?
Draw a picture of the holiday or symbol.
Label your picture.

Talk About It

Talk with your partner about your picture.
Why did you choose that holiday or symbol?

Lesson 5

How Do We Show Pride in Our Nation?

Read Together

Lesson Outcomes

What Am I Learning?
You will explore ways we show pride in our nation.

Why Am I Learning It?
You will understand more about how we can help our country.

How Will I Know that I Learned It?
You will draw about a way you can show you are proud.

Talk About It COLLABORATE

Look closely at the picture. How do the children feel about our country?

Steda Prek/Photodisc/Getty Images

HSS.K.1.2, HSS.K.2, HSS.K.6.2, HAS.HR.2

Analyze the Source

1 Inspect

Read the text.

Look at the pictures.

Who is this text about?

Draw a box around that person.

2 Find Evidence

Reread the text.

Look Again at the pictures.

What did Betsy Ross make?

Circle what she made.

Read Together

The Story of Betsy Ross

Betsy Ross was born in 1752.

In school, she learned to read and write.

Betsy also learned to sew.

She made blankets, curtains, and rugs.

She made tents and flags too.

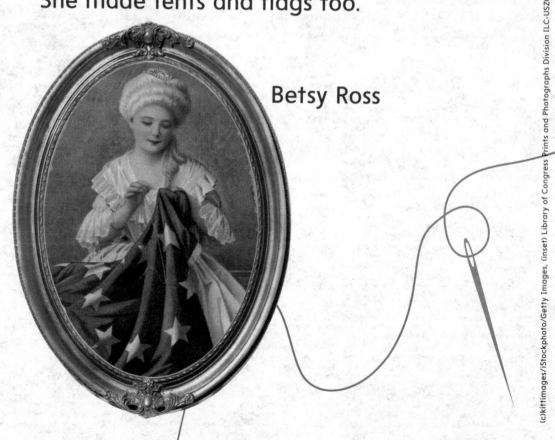

Betsy Ross

(c)kittimages/iStockphoto/Getty Images, (inset) Library of Congress Prints and Photographs Division (LC-USZC4-2998)

People say that Betsy made our country's first flag.

George Washington asked her to make it.

Betsy used George's idea for the flag.

Betsy made the first stars and stripes.

This is the first United States flag.

Christian Mueringer/Alamy

3 Make Connections

Talk Look at the first flag. How is it the same as our flag now? How is it different? What questions do you have about the flag?

COLLABORATE

4 Research Companion

Investigate Read pages 140–147 in your Research Companion.

Look for main topics and key details.

Think About It

Think about what you read.

How can we show we are proud of our nation?

Talk About It COLLABORATE

Talk with your small group about ways we can show we are proud.

✏ Write About It

Choose the idea you think best shows you are proud.

Draw your idea. **Label** your picture.

Siede Preis/Photodisc/Getty Images

Inquiry Project Wrap-Up

It's time for you to share your project! Here's what to do.

☐ Show your picture.

☐ Tell why you think the symbol or holiday best represents America.

☐ Listen to comments and questions.

Tips for Presenting

Remember these tips when you present to your class.

☐ Speak loudly and clearly.

☐ Answer questions with complete sentences.

☐ Relax and enjoy yourself!

Project Rubric

Use these questions to help evaluate your project.

	Yes	No
Did I draw a picture of an American symbol or holiday?		
Did I tell why I think the symbol or holiday represents America?		
Did I use complete sentences to answer questions?		

Project Reflection

Think about what you did in this chapter. What is one thing you did well? What would you change? Tell a partner.

Our Flag

See our flag raised on high?

It waves softly in the sky.

See the colors that are so bright?

I see blue and red and white.

See the stripes above your head?

I count six white and seven red.

And see the stars that shine like gold?

There's one for every state, we're told.

We feel so proud when we see

our flag fly over the land of the free.

Life Long Ago and Today

How Has Our World Changed?

In this chapter, you will explore what life was like long ago! You will read about things from the past and how those things are different today.

Talk About It COLLABORATE

Tell your partner what you want to know about life long ago.

JGI/Jamie Grill/Blend Images/Getty Images

HSS.K.6.3, HAS.CS.2, HAS.CS.3

 **Inquiry Project**

Then and Now

Working with your friends, you will choose something from the past. You will tell what it might be like to use that object today.

Here's your project checklist.

☐ **Choose** something people used long ago. Draw a picture.

☐ **Talk** about how people might use the object now.

☐ **Share** your ideas.

Lesson 1

How Did People Live Long Ago?

Read Together

Lesson Outcomes

What Am I Learning?
You will learn how people lived long ago.

Why Am I Learning It?
You will understand how life today is different from life long ago.

How Will I Know that I Learned It?
You will draw and write about how things change.

HSS.K.6.3, HAS.CS.3, HAS.HR.1

Talk About It

COLLABORATE

Look at the picture.
How is the home different from homes today?
How is it the same?

Joji/iStock/Getty Images

This is a home from long ago.

1 Inspect

Look at the pictures.

What is the same about both pictures?

Circle the things that are the same.

2 Find Evidence

Look Again at the pictures.

What objects do people use to get water?

Draw a box around each object.

Read Together

Things Change

This is a well from long ago.
This is how people got their water every day.
It was located outside.

People got water from a well.

Today we get our water from a faucet.
It is located inside.

3 Make Connections

Talk How did the way people get water change?

COLLABORATE

4 Research Companion

Investigate Read pages 160–165 in your Research Companion.

Look for things that are alike and different.

Getty Images/Moment Open

Think About It

Think about what you read.
How did people live long ago?

Write About It

Draw a picture of something from long ago.
Then draw a picture of the same thing today.
Label your pictures.

Talk About It
COLLABORATE

Find a partner who drew something different.
Talk about how life has changed.

How Do Communities Change?

Read Together

Lesson Outcomes

What Am I Learning?
You will explore communities long ago and today.

Why Am I Learning It?
You will understand how communities change over time.

How Will I Know that I Learned It?
You will draw a picture of your community today and long ago.

Talk About It COLLABORATE

Look at the pictures. How are the cities the same? How are they different?

HSS.K.4.5, HSS.K.6.3, HAS.CS.2, HAS.CS.3, HAS.HI.2, HAS.HR.1

past

present

1 Inspect

Look at the pictures.

How did people get what they needed long ago?

Draw a box around how people got what they needed.

2 Find Evidence

Look Again at the pictures.

How has the way people get what they need changed?

Circle how people get what they need now.

Read Together

Communities Change

Long ago people cut down trees for wood.

Today we can buy wood from a store.

(t)Keystone/Hulton Archive/Getty Images; (b)Juanmonino/E+/Getty Images

Long ago people grew plants for food.

They raised animals too.

Today we can buy food from a grocery store.

3 Make Connections

Talk How does your family get food? How is that different from the way people got food long ago?

COLLABORATE

4 Research Companion

Investigate Read pages 166–173 in your Research Companion.

Look for ways things are alike and different.

Think About It

Think about what you read.

How do communities change?

Talk About It

Talk with your partner about how
communities change.
What do you think your community
was like long ago?

Write About It

Draw a picture of your community today.
Then draw a picture of your community long ago.
Label your picture.

Lesson 3

How Has Travel Changed?

Read Together

Lesson Outcomes

What Am I Learning?
You will explore transportation long ago and today.

Why Am I Learning It?
You will understand how travel has changed.

How Will I Know that I Learned It?
You will draw a type of transportation long ago and how people travel now.

Talk About It COLLABORATE

Look closely at the pictures. Which type of transportation is from the past? Which type of transportation is from today?

HSS.K.6.3, HAS.CS.2, HAS.CS.3

wagon

bus

Read Together

Travel Changes

1 Inspect

Look at the pictures.

How did people travel in the **past**?

(Circle) the picture that shows how people traveled long ago.

2 Find Evidence

Look Again at the pictures.

How is **transportation** different now?

Draw a box around the way people travel today.

The transportation needs of communities are always changing.

past

MandiJubenville/iStock/Getty Images

present

3 Make Connections

Talk How is travel today like travel long ago? How is it different?

COLLABORATE

4 Research Companion

Investigate Read pages 174–179 in your Research Companion.

Look for ways things are alike and different.

Think About It

Think about what you read.
How has travel changed?

Write About It

Draw a type of transportation from long ago.
Then draw how it is different today.
Label your picture.

Talk About It

COLLABORATE

Talk with your partner about your pictures.
How has the type of transportation changed?

How Has Our Nation Changed?

Read Together

Lesson Outcomes

What Am I Learning?

You will learn about our nation long ago.

Why Am I Learning It?

You will understand how our nation has changed.

How Will I Know that I Learned It?

You will draw an answer to a question about our nation.

Talk About It

COLLABORATE

Look at the picture. How is this classroom like your classroom? How is it different?

HSS.K.6.1, HSS.K.6.3, HAS.CS.3, HAS.CS.5, HAS.HR.2, HAS.HI.3

1 Inspect

Read the text.

What did some American Indians eat?

Draw a box around what they ate.

2 Find Evidence

Reread the text.

Why did some American Indians make homes from tree bark?

Circle clues that tell you why.

Read Together

Who Were the First Americans?

American Indians were the first people in our country.
They used the land to help them live.
Some American Indians found plants to eat.
Some made homes from tree bark.

American Indians outside their home in 1902

American Indians getting food from plants in 1908

3 Make Connections

Talk How is your life different from life in our **nation** long ago? How is it the same?

COLLABORATE

4 Research Companion

Investigate Read pages 180–185 in your Research Companion.

Look for causes and effects.

Think About It

Think about what you read.
How has our nation changed?

Talk About It COLLABORATE

What questions do you have about what
our nation was like long ago?
Tell a partner your questions.
Talk about the answers.

Write About It

Draw the answer to one of your questions.
Label your picture.

What Can We Learn from the Past?

Lesson Outcomes

What Am I Learning?
You will learn about people from the past.

Why Am I Learning It?
You will understand how we can learn from the past.

How Will I Know that I Learned It?
You will draw about a person from the past. You will talk about what you can learn from that person.

Talk About It

COLLABORATE

Look at the picture.
What does the picture show you about the past?

HSS.K.6.2, HSS.K.6.3, HAS.CS.1, HAS.CS.2, HAS.HR.1

1 Inspect

Read the text.

Look at the pictures.

What did Annie do last?

Draw a box around that picture.

2 Find Evidence

Reread the text.

Look Again at the pictures.

How did Annie help her family?

Circle those pictures.

Read Together

A Day in the Past

We learn about the past when we read.

June 3, 1872
Today I milked the cow.

I helped Mama make a shirt for Papa.

3 Make Connections

Talk What did Annie do? What lesson can you learn from Annie?

COLLABORATE

4 Research Companion

Investigate Read pages 186–191 in your Research Companion.

Look for what happened first, next, and last.

Think About It

Think about what you read.
What can we learn from the **past**?

Write About It

Choose one person you learned about
in the lesson.
Draw something that person did.
Label your picture.

Talk About It

COLLABORATE

Talk with your partner about the event you drew.
What can you learn from it?

Inquiry Project Wrap-Up

It's time for your team to share your project!
Here's what to do.

☐ Show your picture. Name the object from the past.

☐ Talk about what it might be like to use the
object today.

☐ Listen to what your friends say. Answer their questions.

Tips for Discussing

Remember these tips when you talk with your class.

☐ Take turns speaking.

☐ Listen carefully.

☐ Respond to what others say.

Project Rubric

Use these questions to help evaluate your project.

	Yes	No
Did we choose an object from the past?		
Did we tell what it might be like to use the object today?		
Did we work well together?		

Project Reflection

Think about your work in this chapter. Tell a partner something you did well. Then talk about what you would change next time.

Sing Together

©Kaori Ando/Getty Images

Growing Bigger

(sung to the tune of "Skip to My Lou")

I was one, then I was two.

I was three, then I was four.

Now I've grown up even more.

I have a past and so do you!

Grew, grew, we all grew.

Grew, grew, we all grew.

Grew, grew, we all grew.

I have a past, and so do you!

ESSENTIAL EQ QUESTION

Why Do People Work?

In this chapter, you will explore the work people do! You will read about jobs people do today and what jobs were like in the past.

COLLABORATE

Talk About It

Tell your partner what you know about jobs in our community.

Jayme Thornton/Stockbyte/Getty Images

HSS.K.3

 **Inquiry Project**

When I Grow Up

You will tell what you want to be when you grow up!

Here's your project checklist.

☐ **Think** about what job you want to do.

☐ **Make** a poster about the job.

☐ **Dress** up like the worker.

☐ **Share** your job with the class.

How Do We Work at School?

Lesson Outcomes

What Am I Learning?

You will explore what work is and how we work at school.

Why Am I Learning It?

Learning about work at school will help you understand why your job is important.

How Will I Know that I Learned It?

You will draw three things you do at school.

Talk About It

COLLABORATE

Look closely at the pictures. What are these workers doing? What jobs do they have?

Lesson 1   **167**

1 Inspect

Read the text.

Look at the pictures.

Where can we work?

Underline the words that tell where people work.

2 Find Evidence

Reread the text.

Look Again at the pictures.

What work can people do?

Circle the people doing work.

Read Together

What Is Work?

Work is job that a person does.
People care about their work.
There are many kinds of work.
People work at home.
People work at school.
People work in the community.

David Buffington/Blend Images LLC

(t)SelectStock/Vetta/Getty Images; (b)SunChan/E+/Getty Images

3 Make Connections

Talk What is work? Why do people work?

COLLABORATE

4 Research Companion

Investigate Read pages 206–213 in your Research Companion.

Look for main topics and key details.

Think About It
Think about what you read.

What is work?

How do we work at school?

Talk About It COLLABORATE
Talk with a partner about what you do at school every day.

Write About It
Choose three things you do.

Draw the events in order.

Label each event.

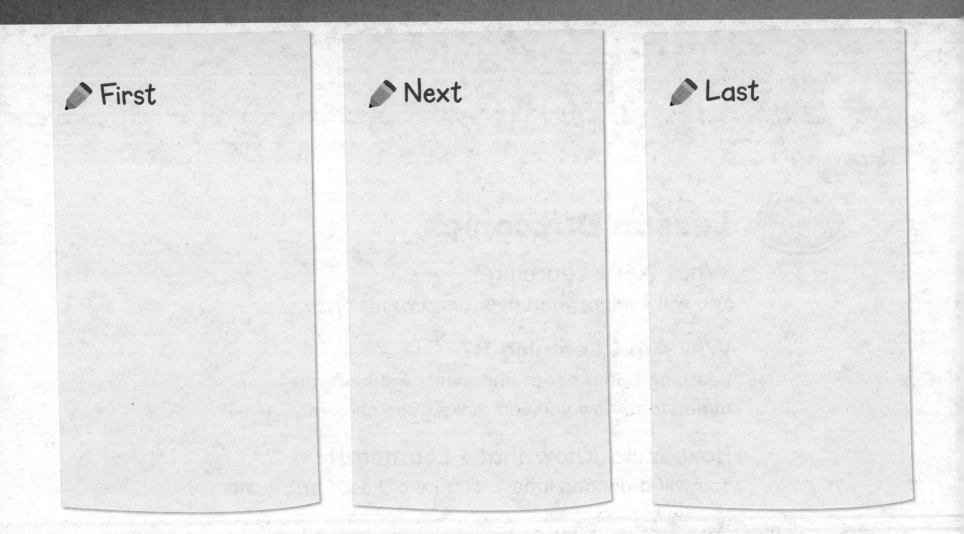

✏️ First

✏️ Next

✏️ Last

Lesson 2

What Are Needs and Wants?

Read Together

Lesson Outcomes

What Am I Learning?
You will explore what needs and wants are.

Why Am I Learning It?
Learning about needs and wants will help you understand how you can make good choices.

How Will I Know that I Learned It?
You will draw and label a picture of needs and wants.

HAS.HI.4

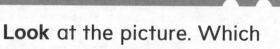

Talk About It   COLLABORATE

Look at the picture. Which picture shows a need?

filmfoto/Getty Images

1 Inspect

Read the text.

Look at the pictures.

Circle pictures that show what people need.

Draw a box around pictures that show what people want.

2 Find Evidence

Reread the text.

Look Again at the pictures.

What do people need?
What do people want?

Read Together

Needs and Wants

Things that we must have to live are called **needs**.
People have many needs.
Things we don't need but would like to have, are called **wants**.

(t)aarrows/Shutterstock.com, (b)serggod/iStock/Getty Images

3 Make Connections

Talk What are things you need to stay healthy? What are some things you want?

COLLABORATE

4 Research Companion

Investigate Read pages 214–221 in your Research Companion.

Think About It

Think about what you read.
What are needs and wants?

Talk About It 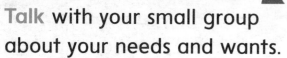 COLLABORATE

Talk with your small group about your needs and wants.

✏️ Write About It

Look at the pictures.
Draw and **label** a picture of a need.
Draw and **label** a picture of a want.

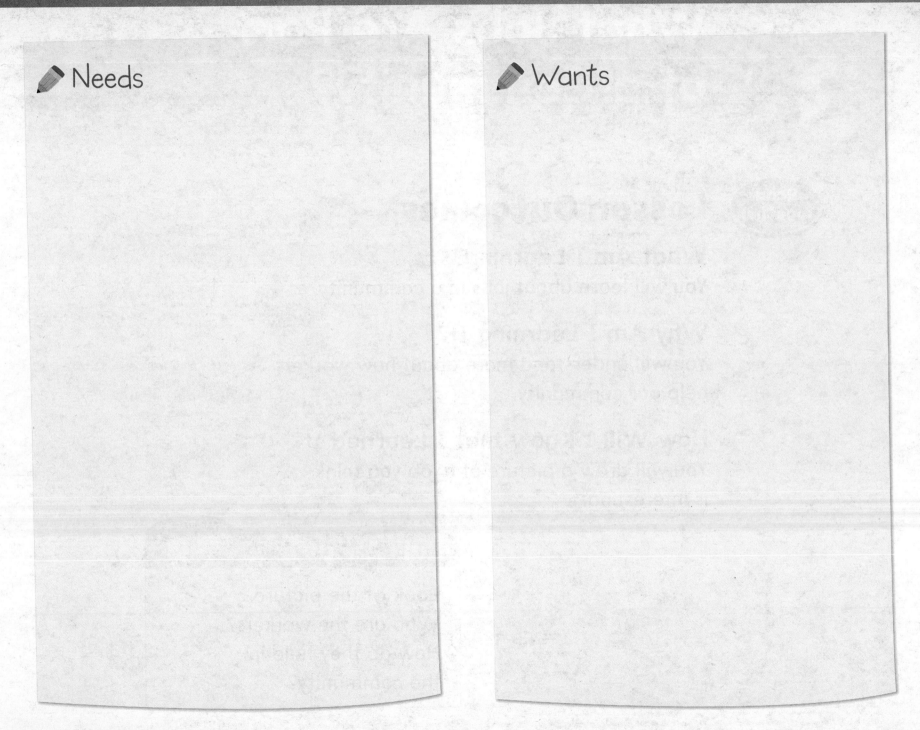

✏️ Needs

✏️ Wants

Lesson 3

What Jobs Are Part of a Community?

 Read Together

Lesson Outcomes

What Am I Learning?
You will learn about jobs in a community.

Why Am I Learning It?
You will understand more about how workers help our community.

How Will I Know that I Learned It?
You will draw a picture of a job you think is interesting.

Talk About It COLLABORATE

Look at the picture. Who are the workers? How do they help in the community?

HSS.K.3, HSS.K.4.5

This is a school librarian.

1 Inspect

Look at the pictures.

What do the service workers do?

(Circle) details about what the workers do.

2 Find Evidence

Look Again at the pictures.

Why are these service workers important?

Draw a box around details that show why the workers are important.

Read Together

Service Workers

A service is work done to help others.
There are many service workers in our community.
Veterinarians are service workers.
They care for animals.
Teachers are service workers, too!
They help children learn.

shironosov/iStock/Getty Images

3 Make Connections

Talk

How are veterinarians and teachers workers alike? How are they different?

4 Research Companion

Investigate Read pages 222–227 in your Research Companion.

Think About It

Think about what you read.

What jobs are part of a community?

Write About It

Choose the job you like the best.

Draw a picture of the job.

Label your picture.

Talk About It

Talk with your partner about the job in your picture.

Why do you like it?

Lesson 4 — How Have Jobs Changed Over Time?

Read Together

Lesson Outcomes

What Am I Learning?
You will explore work long ago and today.

Why Am I Learning It?
You will understand how work has changed over time.

How Will I Know that I Learned It?
You will draw a story about working in the past.

Talk About It
COLLABORATE

Look closely at the pictures. Which picture shows a job in the past? Which picture shows a job today? How do you know?

Siede Preis/Getty Images

HSS.K.3, HSS.K.6.3, HAS.CS.1, HAS.CS.2, HAS.CS.3

This is a fire engine from long ago.

Analyze the Source

1 Inspect

Look at the time line.

What tools do people use today?

(Circle) a tool people use today.

2 Find Evidence

Look Again at the pictures.

What tools did people use long ago? Which tool came first?

Draw a box around the tool that came first.

Read Together **Work Tools**

Jobs change.
The tools people use to do their jobs changed too.
Tools help people do a better job.
Tools have changed over the years.

quill

pen

(l)Burke/Triolo Productions/Brand X Pictures/Alamy Images; (r)Comstock Images/Alamy

laptop
computer

typewriter

(t)Cobalt88/iStock/Getty Images, (b)Jan Tadeusz/Alamy

3 Make Connections

Talk How have work tools changed over time?

COLLABORATE

4 Research Companion

Investigate Read pages 228–233 in your Research Companion.

Look for what happen first, next, and last.

Think About It

Think about what you read.

How have jobs changed over time?

Write About It

Pretend you are from the **past**.

Draw a picture to show a job you do.

Label your picture.

Talk About It COLLABORATE

Talk with your partner about your picture.

Tell your story about working in the past.

What Kinds of Jobs Do People Have?

Read Together

Lesson Outcomes

What Am I Learning?

You will explore jobs people have around the world.

Why Am I Learning It?

You will understand more about how people do their jobs.

How Will I Know that I Learned It?

You will draw and talk about a job you would like to try.

Talk About It

COLLABORATE

Look closely at the pictures. What jobs do the people do?

HSS.K.3, HAS.CS.4

firefighters in India

farmer in Africa

1 Inspect

Read the text.

Look at the pictures.

Circle the places where the pilot goes.

2 Find Evidence

Reread the text.

Look Again at the pictures.

What does the pilot do?

Read Together

Being a Pilot

I am a pilot.

I fly an airplane.

I fly to places all over the **world**!

I meet many interesting people.

Vladimir Maravic/Getty Images

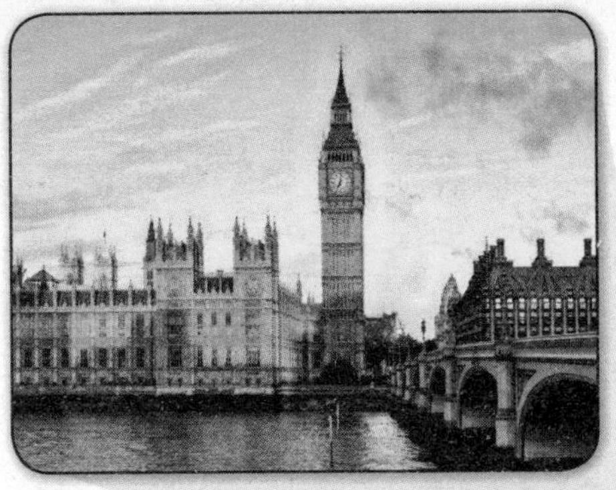

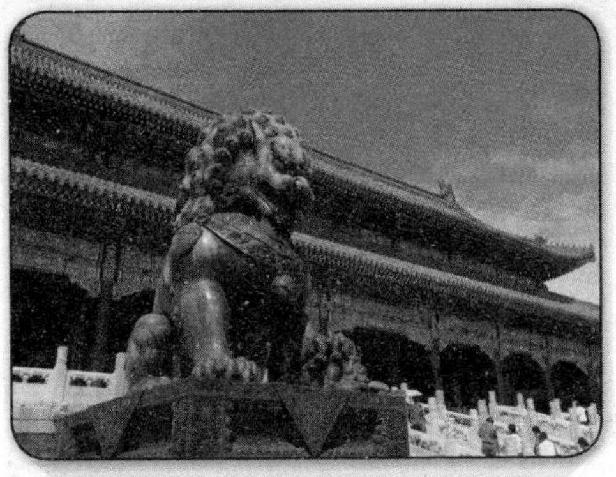

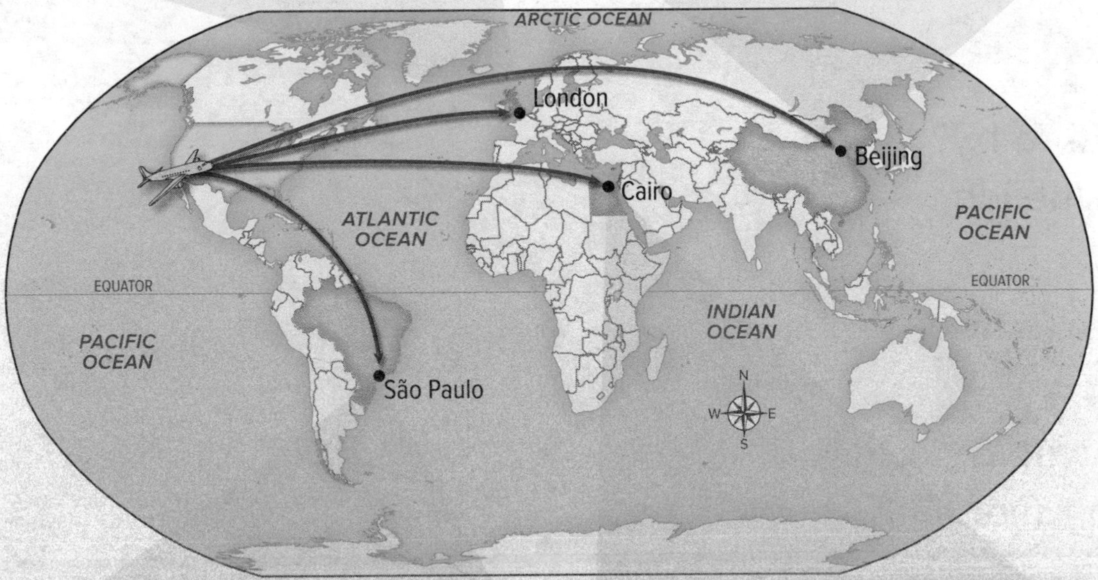
ARCTIC OCEAN
London
Beijing
Cairo
ATLANTIC OCEAN
PACIFIC OCEAN
EQUATOR
INDIAN OCEAN
PACIFIC OCEAN
EQUATOR
São Paulo
N
W
E
S

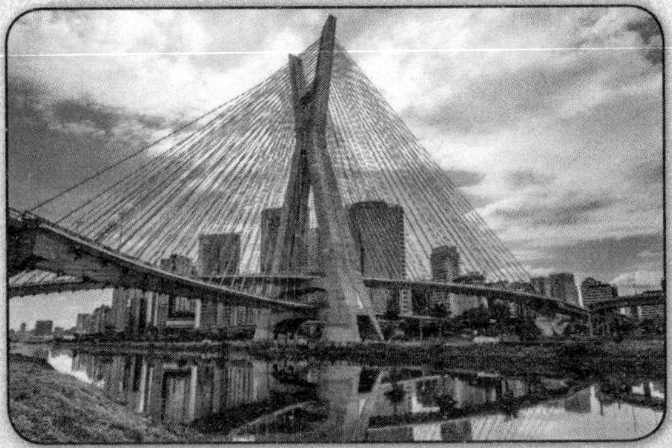

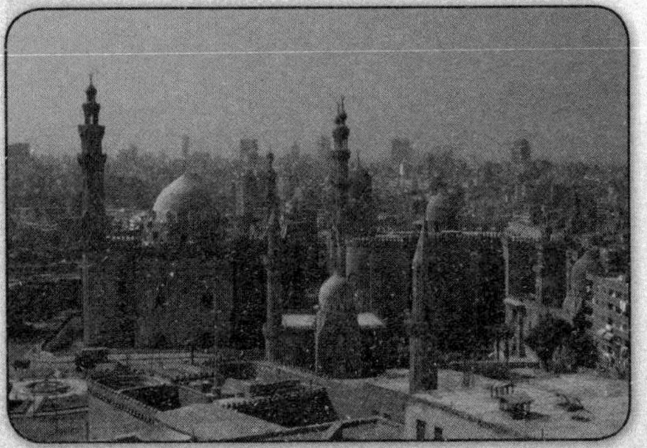

3 Make Connections

COLLABORATE

Talk What do you think the pilot likes about her job? Would you like to be a pilot? Why?

4 Research Companion

Investigate Read pages 234–241 in your Research Companion.

Look for main topics and key details.

Think About It

Think about what you read.
What kinds of jobs do people have
around the world?

Write About It

Which job would you like to try?
Draw a picture to show the job.
Label your picture.

Talk About It

COLLABORATE

Talk about your picture with a partner.
Why would you like to try that job?

ESSENTIAL EQ QUESTION Inquiry Project Wrap-Up

It's time for you to share your project!
Here's what to do.

☐ Show your poster.

☐ Talk about what you want to be and why.

☐ Act out what the worker does.

Tips for Presenting

Remember these tips when you present to your class.

☐ Think about what you want to say.

☐ Speak loudly and clearly.

☐ Use complete sentences.

Project Rubric

Use these questions to help evaluate your project.

	Yes	No
Did I tell what I want to be when I grow up?		
Did my poster show the worker?		
Did I act out what the worker does?		

Project Reflection

Think about what you did in this chapter. What did you do very well? What did you learn about yourself? Tell a partner.

Reference Sources

The Reference Sources has a glossary of vocabulary words from the chapters in this book. Use this section to explore new vocabulary as you investigate and take action.

Glossary

C

citizen a member of a community

cooperate to work together to do something

country an area of land that has a government

courage the ability to do something that is difficult or scary

G

globe a model of the Earth

H

hero a person who does good things

holiday a special day that celebrates someone or something

L

law a rule made by the government

M

map a picture that shows what is in an area

N

nation an area of land that has a government

need something a person must have

neighborhood a part of a town or city

P

past time long ago

present time now

R

responsibility something a person should do

right something a person gets

rule a statement that tells people how to act

S

state an area of a country

symbol something that stands for an idea

T

technology machines made with science

transportation a way of traveling from one place to another

volunteer a person who chooses to help

want something a person wishes to have

work the jobs that people do

world the Earth and all the people in it

Kindergarten
Historical and Social Sciences Content Standards and Analysis Skills

History-Social Science Content Standards.

Learning and Working Now and Long Ago

Students in kindergarten are introduced to basic spatial, temporal, and causal relationships, emphasizing the geographic and historical connections between the world today and the world long ago. The stories of ordinary and extraordinary people help describe the range and continuity of human experience and introduce the concepts of courage, self-control, justice, heroism, leadership, deliberation, and individual responsibility. Historical empathy for how people lived and worked long ago reinforces the concept of civic behavior: how we interact respectfully with each other, following rules, and respecting the rights of others.

K.I Students understand that being a good citizen involves acting in certain ways.

1. Follow rules, such as sharing and taking turns, and know the consequences of breaking them.
2. Learn examples of honesty, courage, determination, individual responsibility, and patriotism in American and world history from stories and folklore.
3. Know beliefs and related behaviors of characters in stories from times past and understand the consequences of the characters' actions.

K.2 Students recognize national and state symbols and icons such as the national and state flags, the bald eagle, and the Statue of Liberty.

K.3 Students match simple descriptions of work that people do and the names of related jobs at the school, in the local community, and from historical accounts.

K.4 Students compare and contrast the locations of people, places, and environments and describe their characteristics.

1. Determine the relative locations of objects using the terms near/far, left/right, and behind/in front.
2. Distinguish between land and water on maps and globes and locate general areas referenced in historical legends and stories.
3. Identify traffic symbols and map symbols (e.g., those for land, water, roads, cities).
4. Construct maps and models of neighborhoods, incorporating such structures as police and fire stations, airports, banks, hospitals, supermarkets, harbors, schools, homes, places of worship, and transportation lines.
5. Demonstrate familiarity with the school's layout, environs, and the jobs people do there.

K.5 Students put events in temporal order using a calendar, placing days, weeks, and months in proper order.

K.6 Students understand that history relates to events, people, and places of other times.

1. Identify the purposes of, and the people and events honored in, commemorative holidays, including the human struggles that were the basis for the events (e.g., Thanksgiving, Independence Day, Washington's and Lincoln's Birthdays, Martin Luther King Jr. Day, Memorial Day, Labor Day, Columbus Day, Veterans Day).
2. Know the triumphs in American legends and historical accounts through the stories of such people as Pocahontas, George Washington, Booker T. Washington, Daniel Boone, and Benjamin Franklin.
3. Understand how people lived in earlier times and how their lives would be different today (e.g., getting water from a well, growing food, making clothing, having fun, forming organizations, living by rules and laws).

Historical and Social Sciences Analysis Skills

In addition to the standards, students demonstrate the following intellectual, reasoning, reflection, and research skills:

Chronological and Spatial Thinking

1. Students place key events and people of the historical era they are studying in a chronological sequence and within a spatial context; they interpret time lines.
2. Students correctly apply terms related to time, including past, present, future, decade, century, and generation.
3. Students explain how the present is connected to the past, identifying both similarities and differences between the two, and how some things change over time and some things stay the same.
4. Students use map and globe skills to determine the absolute locations of places and interpret information available through a map's or globe's legend, scale, and symbolic representations.
5. Students judge the significance of the relative location of a place (e.g., proximity to a harbor, on trade routes) and analyze how relative advantages or disadvantages can change over time.

Research, Evidence, and Point of View

1. Students differentiate between primary and secondary sources.
2. Students pose relevant questions about events they encounter in historical documents, eyewitness accounts, oral histories, letters, diaries, artifacts, photographs, maps, artworks, and architecture.
3. Students distinguish fact from fiction by comparing documentary sources on historical figures and events with fictionalized characters and events.

Historical Interpretation

1. Students summarize the key events of the era they are studying and explain the historical contexts of those events.
2. Students identify the human and physical characteristics of the places they are studying and explain how those features form the unique character of those places.
3. Students identify and interpret the multiple causes and effects of historical events.
4. Students conduct cost-benefit analyses of historical and current events.